BUILDING BLOCKS OF MATH

ADDITION

Written by Joseph Midthun

Illustrated by Samuel Hiti

WORLD BOOK

a Scott Fetzer company
Chicago

World Book, Inc.
180 North LaSalle Street
Suite 900
Chicago, Illinois 60601
USA

For information about other World Book publications,
visit our website at **www.worldbook.com**
or call **1-800-WORLDBK (967-5325).**
For information about sales to schools and libraries,
call 1-800-975-3250 (United States),
or 1-800-837-5365 (Canada).

Library of Congress Cataloging-in-Publication Data
for this volume has been applied for.

Building Blocks of Math
ISBN: 978-0-7166-4447-7 (set, hc.)

Addition
ISBN: 978-0-7166-4448-4 (hc.)

Also available as:
ISBN: 978-0-7166-4454-5 (e-book)

Printed in India by Thomson Press (India) Limited,
Uttar Pradesh, India
1st printing March 2022

WORLD BOOK STAFF
Executive Committee
President: Geoff Broderick
Vice President, Editorial: Tom Evans
Vice President, Finance: Donald D. Keller
Vice President, Marketing: Jean Lin
Vice President, International Sales:
    Eddy Kisman
Vice President, Technology: Jason Dole
Vice President, Customer Success:
    Jade Lewandowski
Director, Human Resources: Bev Ecker

Editorial
Manager, New Content: Jeff De La Rosa
Associate Manager, New Product:
    Nicholas Kilzer
Sr. Editor: William M. Harrod
Proofreader: Nathalie Strassheim

Graphics and Design
Sr. Visual Communications Designer:
    Melanie Bender
Sr. Web Designer/Digital Media Developer:
    Matt Carrington
Coordinator, Design Development and
    Production: Brenda B. Tropinski
Book Design: Samuel Hiti

Acknowledgments:
Created by Samuel Hiti and Joseph Midthun
Art by Samuel Hiti
Additional art by David Shephard/
    The Bright Agency
Additional spot art by Shutterstock
Text by Joseph Midthun

TABLE OF CONTENTS

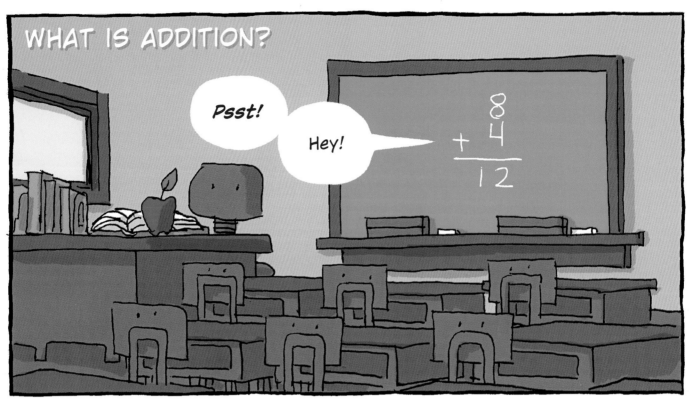

Here are 4 red balloons...

...and here are 8 blue balloons.

woosh

How many balloons are there all together?

How would you add these numbers?

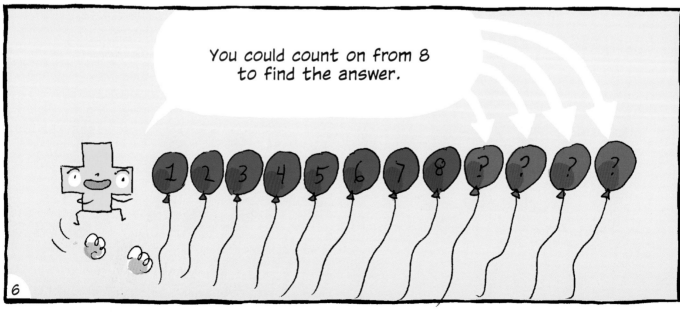

You could count on from 8 to find the answer.

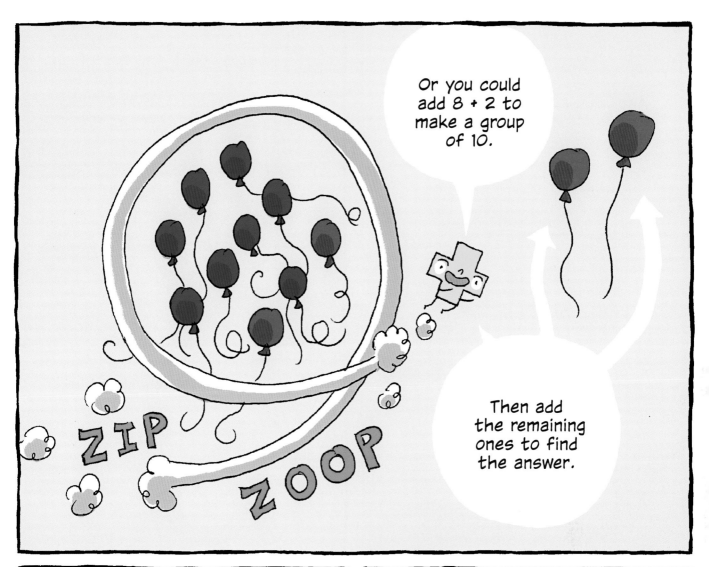

Or you could add 8 + 2 to make a group of 10.

ZIP

ZOOP

Then add the remaining ones to find the answer.

We have 1 ten and 2 ones. How much does that equal?

10 + 2 = 12!

Let's find some more things to add!

ZOOM

TUMP

Ants and aphids!

I love insects!

Let's count the ants first.

How many are there?

12!

Now let's count the aphids!

15!

How many insects are there all together?

Um.

Ah?

9

11

Knowing doubles can help you add fast!

Have you ever heard of doubles?

Double 1 is the same as 2.

Double 2 is the same as 4.

Double 3 is the same as 6.

Double 4 is the same as 8.

Eek!

Double 5 is the same as 10.

Double 6 is the same as 12.

Double 7 is the same as 14.

Double 8 is the same as 16.

Double 9 is the same as 18.

Double 10 is the same as 20!

Let's use doubles to figure out what 5 + 6 equals...

TUMP   TUMP

It's *double 5* plus 1 more.

Snap

What about 5 + 7?

It's 2 more than *double 5*...

...or the same as *double 6!*

Snap   Snap

15

MAKING FRIENDLY NUMBERS

Sometimes numbers can seem unfriendly.

They're tough to add up in your head!

But we can regroup numbers to make them friendlier.

How about you give us an example, wise guy?

Okay.

Say we want to add a row of 11 seeds to this other row of 9 seeds.

Let's find out how many seeds we'll have in all.

MORE FRIENDLY NUMBERS

Look at these two numbers!

Can you add them in your head?

18 is close to 20, so why don't we move 2 ones from 23 over here to 18?

What if you think of the numbers as something else?

Like 23 footballs and 18 tennis balls?

Let's regroup!

18 and 2 is the same as 20.

After regrouping, you have 20 and 20...

...and 1!

20 and 20 equals 40!

Now, all you have to do is solve 40+1!

You can do that in your head!

We didn't change the amount we were adding. We just regrouped the numbers!

Fun, huh?!

Every day, you need to eat 21 fish in order to survive.

Yum!

Uh oh.

Yeesh!

CHOMP
CHOMP
CHOMP
CHOMP
CHOMP
CHOMP

Today, you've already eaten 10 fish.

How many more fish do you need to eat today?

Hmm.

Let's take a closer look and figure it out...

You know you need to eat 21 fish.

And you know you've already eaten 10.

What if you make a jump of 10?

That's right, *double 10!*

Let's try! It's okay if we make a mistake...

Double 10 equals 20.

10 + 10 = 20!

Close, but not perfect...

We're still 1 away from 21.

Hmm.

So, I need to eat 10 fish + 1 fish?

Now, you're getting there!

Ahoy!

Sometimes you can use addition to find out the difference between two amounts.

For instance, look at this group of birds!

There are 15 pelicans in this flock...

...and there are 23 gulls in this flock.

How many more birds are there in the flock of gulls?

Let's compare by matching up the equal amounts.

ADDITION ALL AROUND

Math doesn't make the world go 'round, but it does help you describe it.

And, if you can describe the world around you...

...let's just say, the possibilities are **ENDLESS!**

If you ever come across a problem you can't solve, don't hold it in...

LET IT OUT!

Ask an adult to show you how to solve the problem.

If you keep at it, maybe some day you can show someone else how to solve it!

STAY POSITIVE!

I'm Addition!

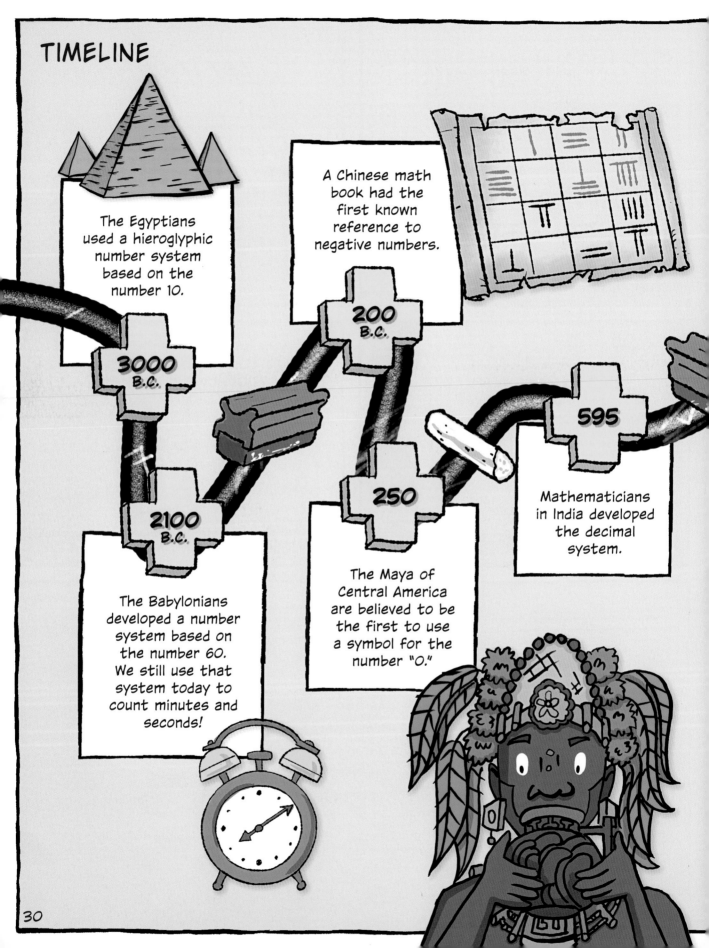

TIMELINE

The Egyptians used a hieroglyphic number system based on the number 10.

3000 B.C.

A Chinese math book had the first known reference to negative numbers.

200 B.C.

2100 B.C.

The Babylonians developed a number system based on the number 60. We still use that system today to count minutes and seconds!

250

The Maya of Central America are believed to be the first to use a symbol for the number "0."

595

Mathematicians in India developed the decimal system.

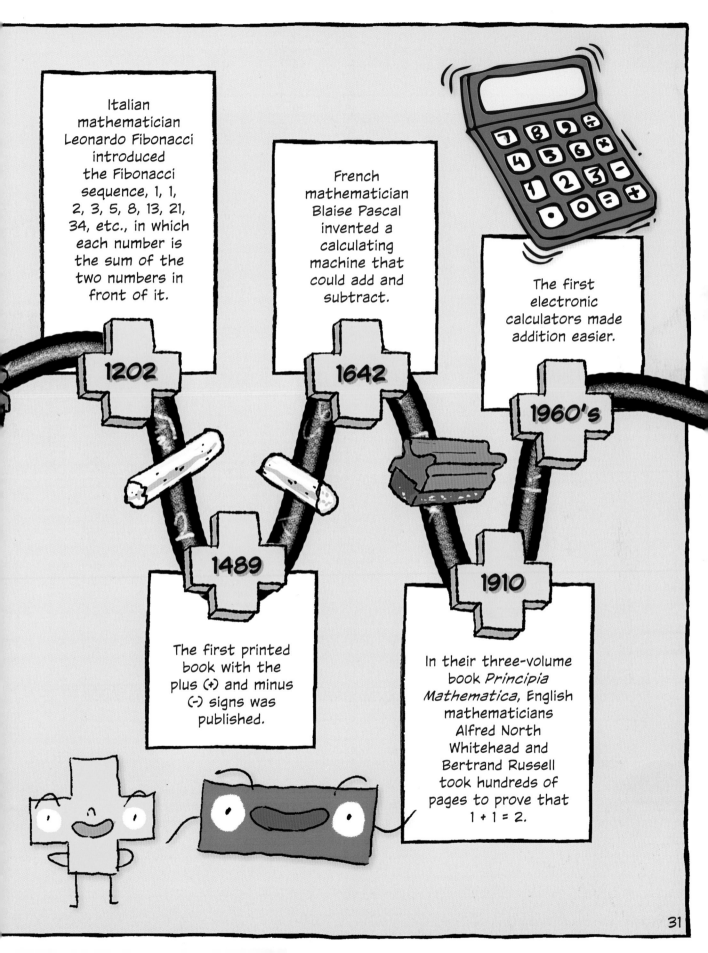

Italian mathematician Leonardo Fibonacci introduced the Fibonacci sequence, 1, 1, 2, 3, 5, 8, 13, 21, 34, etc., in which each number is the sum of the two numbers in front of it.

French mathematician Blaise Pascal invented a calculating machine that could add and subtract.

The first electronic calculators made addition easier.

1202

1642

1960's

1489

1910

The first printed book with the plus (+) and minus (-) signs was published.

In their three-volume book *Principia Mathematica*, English mathematicians Alfred North Whitehead and Bertrand Russell took hundreds of pages to prove that 1 + 1 = 2.

33

I calculated the trajectory for astronaut John Glenn in his pioneering orbital flight around Earth in 1962.

I even calculated the path for Apollo 11, which landed the first two humans on the moon in 1969.

Fact File

Name: Katherine Goble Johnson

Born: 1918 in White Sulphur Springs, USA

Occupation: Mathematician

Claim to fame: NASA mathematician who broke through racial and gender barriers to make many important contributions to space flight.

ACTIVITY: **PUZZLES**

1. What is the next number in each series?

1, 3, 5, 7, 9, _____

15, 18, 21, 24, 27, _____

0, 2, 0, 4, 0, 6, 0, _____

4, 6, 9, 13, 18, _____

2. How many squares are in this picture (do not include rectangles)?

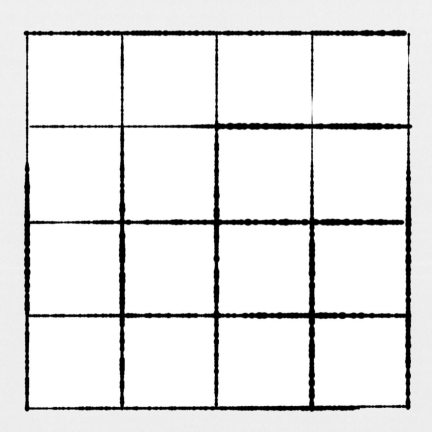

3. What is the value of each shape?

▲ + ▲ = 10

◆ + ▲ = 7

★ + ◆ = 3

4. Let's try one a little harder. Find the sum of the last problem.

🐕 + 🐕 + 🐕 = 30

🦝 + 🐕 = 17

🐖 + 🐖 + 🐕 = 16

🐖 + 🦝 + 🐕 = ?

See page 38 for answers.

ACTIVITY ANSWERS

1. 1, 3, 5, 7, 9, 11 (Add 2 to get the next number)

15, 18, 21, 24, 27, 30 (Add 3 to get the next number)

0, 2, 0, 4, 0, 6, 0, 8 (Add 2 to get the next number after each 0)

4, 6, 9, 13, 18, 24 (The difference between the first two numbers is 2, the next two is 3, the next two is 4, etc.)

2. There are:

16 1x1 squares,   9 2x2 squares,   4 3x3 squares, and 1 4x4 square.

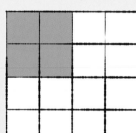 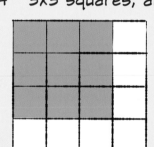 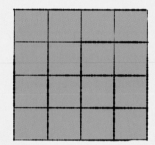

16 + 9 + 4 + 1 = 30 total squares

3. Because the two red triangles add up to 10, each red triangle is 5 (5 + 5 = 10). Because the red triangle is 5, the green diamond must be 2 (2 + 5 = 7). Because the green diamond is 2, the blue star must be 1 (1 + 2 = 3).

▲ = 5

◆ = 2

★ = 1

4. Because the 3 dogs add up to 30, each dog must be 10 (10 + 10 + 10 = 30). Because the dog is 10, the raccoon must be 7 (7 + 10 = 17). Because the dog is 10, each pig must be 3 (3 + 3 + 10 = 16). So, the sum is 3 + 7 + 10 = 20.

 = 10    = 7    = 3

ADDITION FACTS

This table can help you add as easy as 1, 2, 3!

It can also help you learn your addition facts.

HERE'S HOW IT WORKS:

1. Choose a number from the column on the left.
2. Then choose a number from the top row of the table.
3. Find the point where the two numbers meet.

YOU'VE FOUND THE TOTAL OF THE TWO NUMBERS!

+	0	1	2	3	4	5	6	7	8	9	10
0	0	1	2	3	4	5	6	7	8	9	10
1	1	2	3	4	5	6	7	8	9	10	11
2	2	3	4	5	6	7	8	9	10	11	12
3	3	4	5	6	7	8	9	10	11	12	13
4	4	5	6	7	8	9	10	11	12	13	14
5	5	6	7	8	9	10	11	12	13	14	15
6	6	7	8	9	10	11	12	13	14	15	16
7	7	8	9	10	11	12	13	14	15	16	17
8	8	9	10	11	12	13	14	15	16	17	18
9	9	10	11	12	13	14	15	16	17	18	19
10	10	11	12	13	14	15	16	17	18	19	20

FOR EXAMPLE:

1 + 0 = 1; 1 + 2 = 3; 1 + 3 = 4; and so on!

NOTE TO EDUCATORS

This volume supports a conceptual understanding of addition through a series of story problems. As the Addition character solves each story problem, it presents different strategies, including variations of direct modeling, counting, and invented strategies. Below is an index of strategies that appear in this volume.

Index of Strategies

Index